Historic Submarines

Historic Submarines

F. W. Lipscomb

Illustrated by Malcolm McGregor

PRAEGER PUBLISHERS

New York · Washington

BOOKS THAT MATTER

Published in the United States of America in 1970
by Praeger Publishers, Inc., 111 Fourth Avenue,
New York, N.Y. 10003

© 1970 in England, by Hugh Evelyn Limited, London, England

Library of Congress Catalog Card Number: 77-77304

Printed in the Netherlands

Colour Plates

Preface

To cover the evolution of the submarine within the limits of sixteen principal drawings and some 15,000 words of text demands concentration on those advances which have made outstanding contributions to the story. Fortunately, the submarine officers who have kindly given time and thought to the subject are agreed on the choices made for the illustrations and the principal points developed in the text.

So far as the drawings are concerned it must be understood that many submarines during their lifetime were considerably altered, particularly in respect of gun armament, and there are photographs and drawings of some of the submarines illustrated which do not correspond with the illustrations selected for this book.

During the writing of this book and while advising the artist on the 16 full-page drawings, the author has consulted numerous naval officers and civilians from many countries who have made detailed studies of the subject. Some of these have collected thousands of photographs, others have compiled whole libraries of books, articles and paper-cuttings, covering many aspects of design and capability. Nevertheless, in spite of this wealth of material, it is clear that there are still some features of design which have not been recorded and the precise origin of some important fittings cannot be exactly established. For example, it is generally agreed that Professor Marié Davy introduced the periscope in the French Navy in 1854, Drzewiecki and Goubet made primitive periscopes around 1879 and Captain Bacon designed his own for the British 'Holland' boats, but it is a matter of opinion as to who was the most significant innovator.

As regards hydroplanes, the French were again prominent in this development. Goubet and Gustave Zédé employed them in their drawings. Elsewhere Nordenfeldt and Holland made contributions and Waddington fitted hydroplanes to his submarine which he built in Liverpool in 1886.

Study of the schnorkel tube leads us to no firm conclusion as to its origin. Simon Lake fitted a tube to his *Argonaut* in 1895 and this may be considered to be the first example. Much later, in 1916, the well-known firm of Scott designed a fully operational tube. Nevertheless it was not until the Second World War that this fitting took its place as standard equipment, when the Germans appreciated its value in extending the endurance of their submarine fleet.

Turning to modern times, it must be understood that nuclear submarines are equipped with much classified material and information on such matters as sonar and radar has had to be omitted, from both the illustrations and the text.

Acknowledgements

…riting this book and assisting Malcolm McGregor to ob-
…sufficient and accurate material for his drawings, I have
…ved generous help from many officers and civilian tech-
…ns. Unfortunately, space does not permit mention of all
…must ask the forbearance of those who are not named in
…on.

…am especially grateful to Admiral Sir Charles Little,
…., G.B.E., one time Commanding Officer of *Holland IV*, for
…nvaluable help with the drawing of the 'Holland' type
…or his experienced advice generally. Also Vice Admiral
…Hugh Mackenzie, K.C.B., D.S.O., D.S.C., lately head of the
…sh Nuclear Submarine Programme, who kindly checked
…manuscript and gave most helpful advice, particularly on
…ear matters. As ever the Ministry of Defence (Navy) gave
…y assistance and I am grateful to Miss J. N. Price for her
…ial interest. Mr Raymond V. B. Blackman, M.I.Mar.E.,
…N.A., editor of *Jane's Fighting Ships*, Mr E. Clarke, Public
…tions Officer, Vickers Armstrongs, and Lieutenant
…mander G. H. F. Frere-Cork, R.N. (Retd.), Curator, Sub-
…ne Museum, H.M.S. *Dolphin*, have all made most
…able contributions and I owe them special thanks. Mr
…orn and Mr Tucker of the National Maritime Museum,
…Mr J. Fulford, Director, and Mr R. Mayne of the Impe-
…War Museum, gave ready help at all times which was
…h appreciated. The help provided by Mr L. Honeywill of
…ton Abbot, Devonshire, one time Chief Engineroom
…ficer, who is an expert on historical detail, was extremely
…ul.

…road, my thanks go first to Monsieur Henri le Masson,
…President of the Académie de Marine and editor of *Les
…tes de Combat*, who not only entrusted to me some irre-
…eable documents but also sent me a copy of the manu-
…t of his own latest book *Du Nautilus au Redoutable*.
…sieur le Masson also read the manuscript of my book and
…e many most important suggestions and comments.

…embers of the Staff of the Commander-in-Chief United
…es Naval Forces Europe could not have been more help-
…nd I am specially indebted to Captain S. H. Packer, U.S.N.,
…Commander H. E. Hetu, U.S.N. Mr Claud M. Ladd of the
…e of the Assistant Secretary of Defence, Washington,
…, sent most useful lists and comments. Mr S. J. Worman
…Captain Frank Lynch, U.S.N. (Retd.), both of the General
…amics, Electric Boat Division, Groton, Connecticut, did
…their power to answer the many questions put to them.
…e Defence and Naval Attachés of Germany, Italy and
…n, resident in London, put me in touch with experts in
…r respective countries, notably Herr W. Grutzemacher of
…enhofen.

Finally, I wish to record my warmest thanks to the publishers, particularly Mr Hugh Street, the Managing Director, for his understanding of the problems involved, and Miss
Virginia Sherwin for much typing and retyping.

F.W.L.
East Horsley
April 1969

While endorsing the acknowledgments above, I should like
also to express my gratitude to those other people who have
made valuable contributions to the preparation of the colour
drawings in this book.

I am indebted to Mr Anthony Preston of the National
Maritime Museum for his enthusiastic interest and much
invaluable advice. A special debt of thanks is owed to Captain K. Miyo of Japan, who, despite some personal incon-
venience, was able to gather sufficient references to make it
possible to draw the Japanese I 400 submarine; a last-
minute disaster was thereby narrowly averted. Mr John
Batchelor was unstinting with material from his own collec-
tion and was able to put me in touch with other experts. As
ever I found Historical Research Unit ready with help and
sound advice when things became difficult. Mr White of the
Ministry of Defence (Air) helped with aircraft references and
put me on to other lines of enquiry. My thanks go to Miss
Tilbury of *Flight* magazine who supplied me with some
excellent photographs, thus resolving an earlier crisis.
Finally, here, I should like to record my gratitude to the
staffs of the various libraries and museums, in this country
and abroad, who gave valuable help. It seems their lot in life
to remain unnamed but it is their willing co-operation and
interest which contributes so much towards smoothing the
researcher's stony path.

Lastly, but by no means least, I am indebted to my wife for
several difficult technical translations and for her understanding in the face of the tide of books and reference material which for many months threatened to disrupt a normally
well-run home.

Malcolm McGregor
June 1969

ow it all began

Visitors to the Bibliothèque Royale, Brussels, can enjoy some amusing reflections from a picture in a thirteenth-century manuscript, *Le Vraie Histoire d'Alexandre*, showing this great conqueror under water in a glass barrel which has been lowered on chains to the bottom of the sea from an attendant boat on the surface.

Long before this supposed adventure the idea of navigating under water had attracted inventors, but all failed to construct a suitable vessel because they had not the material means. It was not until an Englishman, William Bourne, who had served as a gunner under the Elizabethan Admiral, Sir William Monson, had produced a treatise in the year 1580 stating exactly how ballast water could be controlled by screws operating leather bulkheads, that the possibility became a fact. Bourne's writings undoubtedly attracted the attention of Cornelius Van Drebbel, a Dutch mechanician and chemist, who adopted the ballast water principle and the idea of using leather bulkheads. Bourne said it was well known that a ship which floats displaces exactly its own weight of water. He went on to give a lucid explanation of why a ship floats and what can be done to make it 'sink or swim'.

Of the methods expounded by Bourne to make a ship do either of these things at will, Van Drebbel chose that of taking in water and discharging it again and designed a number of submarines on this principle, one of which he brought to London and demonstrated before King James I. The buoyancy of this boat could be reduced by withdrawing a leather bulkhead and taking in water through holes in the ship's side until the upper deck was awash. Then, propelled by oars, the holes for which were made watertight again by leather, the boat proceeded awash but at times completely disappeared for a few moments. Full buoyancy was recovered by screwing the leather bulkhead out to its former position.

This was considered to be very remarkable and it certainly was so for those times. There is no doubt that Van Drebbel's boat actually went from Westminster to Greenwich in this manner, but the story that King James I or even passengers went in the boat for this trip is not generally believed. Built of wood with iron frames and lined with greased leather it is said that the boat was comparatively dry inside. Being a chemist Van Drebbel improved on Bourne by introducing a chemical which circulated through the boat from an intake air pipe with the effect of purifying the air. The cycle was completed by means of bellows and an exhaust pipe. Thus an Englishman thought out the first practicable design for a submarine and a Dutchman made the first operational boat.

Van Drebbel died in 1634 and bequeathed his inventions to his son-in-law Dr Kuffler, with whom Samuel Pepys, the diarist, had 'discourses in the coffeehouse', chiefly to hear about inventions for blowing up ships, but the meeting is evidence of the interest in naval circles in England of Van Drebbel's work. Much was claimed by Bourne for his invention, such as exploring the bottom of the sea, but in the navy men reasoned that, as command of the sea was now dictated by the gun, a vessel which could submerge and thereby defeat the power of this weapon would have a great influence on sea power. However, the submarine was in such a primitive state that these very potent thoughts could not, at that time, be translated into something practical.

It was a Frenchman, de Son, who in 1653 was the first to provide mechanical power to propel a submarine. His boat, like Van Drebbel's, navigated only awash. It was 72 feet long and was fitted with an internal paddle wheel which worked in a well in the centre of the vessel. This paddle wheel was intended to be turned by a clockwork mechanism, but the power, which was sufficient when the wheel was in air, was totally inadequate when the wheel was in water. The boat was designed never to be in more than the awash position and must therefore be classed with the submersibles (ie. vessels that can submerge for brief periods) rather than with submarines proper.

From 1680 all manner of people were putting their brains to

the submarine problem. This plethora of designs, and in some cases the building of actual vessels, went on until the advent of the mechanical age. To follow the development objectively it is necessary to be selective and credit must go to two French priests, Fathers Mersenne and Fournier of the Order of Minimes, who, shortly after Van Drebbel's death, produced a design for a submarine with wheels for movement along the sea bed. The boat was to have air-pumps and ventilators, phosphorescent apparatus for lighting inside, a battery of big guns to be fired on either side, with special valves to prevent the water coming in when the guns recoiled, and arrangements for a man to leave the boat submerged and return at will.

Many other inventors produced designs but none offered a true advance until the Abbé Borelli propounded a scheme for destroying the buoyancy by filling a number of leather bottles and returning to full buoyancy by expelling the water from these bottles by hand. Nevertheless no construction took place until, in 1747, an Englishman by the name of Symon built a boat. In this design he employed the idea of controlling the buoyancy by a number of leather bottles on the Borelli principle. Thus a practical step nearer the ballast tank had been taken.

Inevitably this pioneer work was dangerous and in 1773 disaster befell a ship's carpenter named Day. This man pioneered the use of detachable ballast. Large stones with ringbolts which were hung outside his submarine could be slipped from inside. Day made a successful dive in Plymouth Sound and then moved to a deeper and more exposed part of the harbour. When he got there he found his boat needed more ballast stones to make it submerge in the saltier water of the open sea and ordered more to be attached. The boat sank in 22 fathoms of water and did not reappear. It is reasonable to suppose that the pressure of water at that depth collapsed the hull. Two points emerged from Day's unfortunate experience. Firstly, had time allowed him to release his ballast he would have shot to the surface. This manoeuvre was the forerunner of devices to regain buoyancy quickly by releasing a heavy weight specially provided for this purpose. Secondly, the importance of allowing for water pressure at depth became apparent. Submarines have always been limited in their operations by this factor.

Bourne's system of ballast water control
A. *Air holes*
B. *Bulkhead which is screwed in and out*
C. *Capstan for screwing bulkhead in and out*
D. *Ballast*
H. *Inlet holes for water*
L. *Leather*
M. *Hollow mast for air supply*
W. *Space occupied by water when craft is submerged*
S. *Screws*

Below
De Son's submarine, showing internal paddle wheel

Bottom
Symon's submarine, 1747
A. Leather bottles for carrying water ballast
B. Oar aperture made watertight with leather

CHAPTER II

Progress through war

Progress in invention is always stimulated in wartim[e] the American War of Independence was no exception. [David] Bushnell, who graduated at Yale College in 1775, comm[enced] there his study of the problems of a submersible vessel w[hich] he completed later. When the English blockaded the ea[stern] seaboard in 1776 he thought that it might be possible to [break] this stranglehold by placing explosive charges under[neath] the British men-of-war – a type of weapon with which h[e had] also been experimenting. To Bushnell's way of thinkin[g un] doubtedly one method of carrying out this plan would [be to] fix the explosive charges by means of his submarine. [Bush] nell's boat was made of wood and shaped like two gig[antic] walnut shells standing on end. To strengthen it a stout [piece] of wood was placed across the interior so that the sides w[ould] not buckle inwards due to water pressure. This pie[ce of] wood also served as a seat for the operator. Bushnell c[alled] his submarine the *Turtle* as he considered it was shape[d like] one. A hole in the bottom admitted water when he w[anted] the boat to submerge, and two brass pumps were instal[led for] ejecting it when he wished to surface. The operator adm[itted] water by placing his foot on a brass valve and depressi[ng it] and ejected it by using the pumps. On the outside of th[e bot] tom end of his *Turtle* Bushnell placed 700 lb of lead ba[llast] 200 lb of which could be slipped by means of a cord [from] inside the boat, on the lines of Day's principle, so tha[t the] operator could rise rapidly in an emergency. The boat [con] tained enough air for one man for half an hour while [sub] merged. When the water tank at the bottom of the boa[t was] full the top of the *Turtle*, which had a small brass con[ning] tower sufficiently large to contain a man's head, was[awash. This conning tower was fitted with glass window[s. To] go forwards or backwards Bushnell fitted an oar 'formed [on] the principle of the screw' which turning one way prop[elled] the *Turtle* forwards and the other way backwards. Thi[s] 'screw' could be operated by either hand or foot. There w[as a] rudder with a tiller which was long enough to be held u[nder] the operator's arm.

A second oar, again designed 'on the principle of the scr[ew'] was fitted in a vertical position near the conning tow[er to] assist the operator to move the boat in the vertical p[lane.] Finally, to fix the explosive charge, a small wooden s[crew] was to be inserted into the hull of the enemy ship an[d re] leased from the *Turtle* together with the explosive ch[arge] which was attached to it. By the aid of a time clock the [sub] marine was given half an hour to escape after which [the] explosive went off.

Here then was a forerunner of things to come, a [sub] mersible capable of manoeuvre under its own power, [sub] merged by means of a controlled ballast tank and armed [with] a weapon believed to be capable of sinking a battleship.

In 1776 the English fleet was anchored in the Hudson R[iver] and Bushnell determined to put his invention to the test[. He] did not man the *Turtle* himself but secured the services [of] Sergeant Ezra Lee. The submarine was towed by two row[ing] boats to within a few miles of the enemy and then, with [the] aid of the tide and the versatile Lee's efforts with the scr[ew] and tiller, it swept towards the English fleet, only to be [car] ried past the ships by the strength of the tide. However, [Lee] waited in the awash position until the tide had slackened [and] then managed to manoeuvre his submarine, by now [sub] merged again, under H.M.S. *Eagle*, a 64-gun two-decker [ship] of the line carrying the flag of Lord Howe. The attack fa[iled] only because Lee could not get the detachable scre[w to] penetrate the copper bottom of the warship, and he gave [up.] When the tide turned in his favour he returned to base [. On] the way he was sighted by some soldiers on the shore who [put] out in a boat. Lee instantly slipped the detachable screw [and] the charge and managed to reach safety; meanwhile the [time] clock ran its course and the charge exploded. Later two m[ore] attempts were made but both failed and the experiment [was] not repeated. Nevertheless Bushnell goes down in histor[y as] the first inventor of a submarine which went into action[.

One year before Ezra Lee attacked H.M.S. *Eagle* Ro[bert]

hnell's submarine, 1776
Screw to which magazine was attached
Magazine
Screw-shaped oar for going ahead or astern
Screw-shaped oar for forcing the boat under water
Rudder
Pumps
Water ballast tanks
Seat for operator

Fulton was born in Little Britain (now named Fulton), Pennsylvania. He was an inventor in every sense of the word. His genius led him to construct flax-spinning devices, saw-mills, rope-making machines and much else. He had progres-sive ideas on canals and dams and was a landscape painter in his own right. His travels brought him via England to France where he found the English were this time blockading the French northern ports. Like Bushnell before him, he deter-mined to try and break the blockade by means of a submarine carrying explosive charges. He wrote on 13th December 1797: 'Citizen Director. Having taken great interest in all that would diminish the power of the English Fleet I have planned the construction of a mechanical engine, in which I have the greatest confidence for the annihilation of this Navy.'

He went on to say that to do this he had formed 'The Nauti-lus Company'. He would charge the French government 4000 francs a gun for every English ship over 40 guns and propor-tional amounts for other ships. If the French government built their own Nautiluses this would cost them 10,000 francs for each one, payable to the inventor. As this form of attack was considered to be 'against the Laws of War' he asked for arrangements to be made that any man captured during these operations should be considered to be a prisoner of war and not hung or otherwise put to death.

These first proposals were turned down by the French so he approached the Dutch government, who also rejected them. Not too depressed, Fulton returned to France and made a personal approach to Bonaparte who licensed a grant of 10,000 francs of public money to enable Fulton to make a start with his first boat. She was laid down in 1800 and com-pleted in the same year. The submarine was 21 feet 4 inches long and 7 feet in diameter. The hull was made of copper with iron frames. Like Bushnell's *Turtle* there was a detachable keel which could be slipped in an emergency. Water ballast was admitted into tanks and a double pump was fitted to discharge it. She was considered strong enough to go to 25 feet in depth. For the first time in submarine development horizontal hydroplanes were fitted aft. A further innovation was the anchor gear which could be let go from inside the boat. Motive power was provided by a two-bladed propeller in the stern which was turned by hand. On the surface it was in-tended that the boat would manoeuvre by sail for which there was a collapsible mast stowed on the upper deck when the submarine was dived. To work the boat there was a crew of three men.

Fulton's *Nautilus* was as near to something really practic-able in submarine design as anyone could go in his day and age. The introduction of hydroplanes to help the vessel main-tain even depth and the fitting of a propeller were great advances. It can be said, further, that this was the first submarine to have two sources of motive power. The striking-power against an enemy was similar to Bushnell's except that Fulton employed a strong spike for driving into the bottom of the hull of a ship, and to this the explosive charge was attached by a stout line. The explosive was fired by means of a lanyard and gunlock instead of a clockwork device.

Fulton first demonstrated his *Nautilus* on 13th June 1800 opposite the Hotel des Invalides between the present Concorde and Alma bridges. Other dives took place at Rouen and Le Havre in July and August. Later *Nautilus* was stationed at Brest and dived successfully in the open sea. These diving tests were witnessed with considerable astonishment. Finally an old schooner was placed at his disposal which he blew up by towing an explosive charge underneath. This was towed by a barge but it showed the possibilities for use by a submarine.

Eventually Fulton was allowed to try and sink one or more of the English frigates off Brest but he never got near enough to them to fix his charge.

Finally Fulton's plans had a mixed reception in circles because of the moral objection to this kind of war. Admiral Pleville le Pelley, for example, who had been ister of Marine in 1798, declared that his conscience w not allow him to have recourse to so terrible an inven On the other hand Monsieur Forfait, a prominent N Constructor, was enthusiastic.

Before going home to America Fulton decided on one try in England and in 1804 laid his plans before the Br government. Pitt, then Prime Minister, was attracted b demonstrations but Admiral Earl St Vincent, then Lord of the Admiralty, while recognising Fulton's inve genius said with great emphasis, 'Pitt was the greatest that ever existed to encourage a mode of warfare which t who commanded the seas did not want, and which, if suc ful, would deprive them of it.' This profound statement to influence British naval affairs for the next hundred y and more, and is itself sufficient to justify Fulton's r being added to the list of those who contributed to th velopment of this underwater weapon.

Fulton's NAUTILUS, 1800
A. Mast
B. Conning tower
C. Spike for putting into the bottom
   of a hostile ship
D. Keel

E. Kingston valves
F. Vertical rudder
G. Anchor
H. Inclined plane diving rudders
K. Hand wheel for rotating propeller (P)
N. Gearing for working vertical rudder

ter the mechanical age

During the first half of the nineteenth century, when the beginnings of the mechanical age were making their mark on naval affairs, submarine development made little progress until 1850 when a Bavarian, William Bauer, built the first iron submarine. Bauer was inspired from the same motives as Bushnell and Fulton, namely naval blockade. This time Germany and Denmark were at war and the superior Danish fleet was blockading the German seaboard.

Bauer's submarine was 26½ feet long and had a displacement of 38½ tons. Symon's principle for submerging by taking in ballast water as developed by Bushnell and Fulton was now fully accepted, so this boat was fitted with tanks with inlet valves in double bottoms for destroying the buoyancy and pumps for discharging the water. Having brought the boat to a state of equilibrium with the upper deck awash, Bauer moved a heavy weight which gave the boat an inclination. As soon as she started to go under he moved it back and so the boat submerged in a succession of dips. This was different from Van Drebbel's oars and Bushnell's vertical screws, and did not rely on Fulton's principle of forward motion by propeller and horizontal stability by hydroplanes, although Bauer had a propeller at the stern which was hand-operated. He also had an explosive charge for securing to the bottom of an enemy ship, the difference between it and Fulton's being that it was fired by an electric battery.

Bauer made a feint at the Danish ships and this had the desired effect of making them lie off at a respectful distance. The submarine's influence was growing. While this development itself made history in the sphere of naval operations it was on the technical side where Bauer also made his name. On 1st February 1851, when off Kiel, Bauer and two seamen dived in the submarine but, on reaching the deepest part of the harbour, the sheet iron hull began to give way and water came in. The boat sank to the bottom out of control in 54 feet of water. Bauer kept his head and ordered his men to let in more water so that the whole interior was flooding. The two seamen, terrified, refused to obey but Bauer managed, even in this desperate situation, to convince them that this was their only hope of survival. Indeed the danger now came more from the anchors and grapnels which those on the surface threw down in an effort to grasp the boat and raise it. In due time the water entering the boat compressed the air inside to such an extent that the pressure inside equalled that of the water outside and, without any aid from Bauer, the weakly constructed hatch flew open, releasing the bubble of air and taking Bauer and his two companions with it. They had been down five hours and had made the first free escape from a sunken submarine.

In common with other pioneers Bauer was discredited in his own country and, after some time spent in England where his brains were tapped but he was not employed, he persuaded the Russians to let him build a submarine. The result was a submarine similar to the first but bigger, being 52 feet long and with a beam of 12 feet. The boat was launched in 1855, and a year later, during the coronation of Alexander II on 6th September 1854, he took several musicians with him and submerged to the harbour bed. When the guns began the Royal Salute his band struck up with the National Anthem. This lark was not without its technical aspect, as the ships in harbour heard the strains of music, and although Bauer himself had already been interested in the rising science of underwater sound waves his novel idea gave impetus to the subject.

It was now that the French, following in the wake of de Son and the Abbé Borelli, began to take a major interest in submarines. Their contribution which followed has not, in the opinion of many, been fully recognised outside their own country.

In 1858 Captain (later Vice Admiral) Bourgois designed 'Le projet du Plongeur'. This was examined by officers of the Corps of Naval Constructors, and the development was recommended by Brun, a naval Commander and member of the Corps of Constructors (later Director of Naval Construction). The design was accepted and the keel was laid in June 1860. This boat was 140 feet long and displaced 420 tons. The propulsion was by compressed air which drove a propeller. The engine was designed by Brun. The submarine was made of iron plates fastened to a heavy keel which extended right forward to support the spar which carried the explosive charge—an ambitious project.

In a hollow part of the hull a salvage boat was fitted, capable of taking twelve men. The boat was bolted to the hull and pressure inside the submarine was kept just above that of the water outside so that there was no seepage of water at the bolts into the vessel.

The *Plongeur* had trouble. She was fitted with a system of moving water from one end of the boat to the other by means of pipes and pistons to control the longitudinal equilibrium. This system worked too slowly so that the boat plunged about. The hydroplanes in the stern were found to have insufficient power to eliminate this so a vertical screw was added. This did not cure the trouble. Besides this difficulty, naval officers considered that the explosive, which was carried on a spar in the bow, was too weak to justify further development of the submarine weapon at that stage. Nevertheless she was the first submarine which did not rely on human power for propulsion. The year was 1863.

It is necessary to leave the French development for a brief period at this point because at this time, in the New World, America was in a state of civil war and by 1864 the north, having built up their naval forces, set about blockading the south. For the third time this form of naval warfare mad impact on the development of the submarine. Both sides built ironclads and the famous fight between the Fed *Monitor* and the Confederate *Virginia* had already rev tionised naval thinking. But more than this, the Confe ates were the first to appreciate that the submarine wa be the weapon of the weaker power and they built t 'Davids'. This biblical name was the obvious choice for a marine designed to attack an ironclad. The 'Davids' were proper submarines as they could only 'trim down', ther reducing their silhouettes to a minimum. Some were pro led by hand and others by steam. One steam *David* dama the Federal armed ship *Ironsides*, and another, hand pelled, sank the wooden *Housatonic* by charging the with its bow explosive which opened a hole in the eng room but at the same time sank the *David* with all hand is not without significance that this particular *David* been sunk while exercising no less than three times, considerable loss of life, due to total lack of experience, n particularly operating in the awash condition with hatches open. But each time new crews were forthcom The navies of the world followed these events with greatest interest and noted that when the victorious Fede overran the Confederate dockyards they found a full-s submarine programme under way. Weaker naval pov took careful note of the possibilities open to them thro the development of the submarine, while Britain pond on the words of Lord St Vincent.

Bourgois's PLONGEUR, 1860
A. *Hatches for crew to enter by*
B. *Hand-wheel for rotating the propeller*
C. *Steering wheel and rods to rudder (K)*
D. *Pump for ejecting water ballast*
E. *Heavy weight for altering longitudinal trim*
F. *Gearing for moving weight (E)*
G. *Water ballast tanks*

Opposite page
The Confederate 'Davids', c. 1865
a & b: A steam 'David'
c, d & e: A hand-propelled 'David'
(Hydroplanes are marked X)
f: The spar torpedo of a 'David'
(the chemical fuses for exploding the charge are marke

CHAPTER IV

Introduction to the Twentieth Century: France and America show the way

Some fifteen years later a notable development took place in France. This was not surprising since France had always been in the lead in naval construction in Europe, particularly at the height of the sailing ship era. Monsieur Claude Goubet, a civil engineer, designed two submarines, the *Goubet I* and *II*. Both were very small, one idea being that such a boat could be hoisted on board a battleship and used as an invisible torpedo boat. Only 16½ feet in length and weighing 11 tons *Goubet I* was propelled by electric power from a battery of Laurent-Cély accumulators. She was provided with a small periscope. A circular hole in the bows allowed a steel bar to be run out about 10 feet which carried a scissor device for cutting enemy nets. This boat was built in Paris and took the water on the Seine for the first time on 20th March 1887. Trials were run in October 1888, after which she was sent to Cherbourg where, between 1889 and 1892, she was set an agreed programme but did not succeed in completing it, being unsteady both in course and diving depth, with the result that the Minister of Marine refused to accept her.

The second *Goubet*, 26 feet long, was also built on the Seine, this time at Agenteuil. Unhappily she was unsuccessful for much the same reasons as *Goubet I*, and when the French Navy tried her out in 1899 at Toulon she, too, was not accepted. Nevertheless, had she succeeded in her trials the proposal was to fit her with two torpedoes, to be launched from dropping gear. Thus the first submarine fitted with electric power and designed to carry torpedoes never entered service, but credit must go to Goubet for his part in the story of the evolution of the submarine.

It must not be supposed that by this time there had been no other submarines constructed or designed than those mentioned in this book. On the contrary, this process of development had been going on ever since Van Drebbel's day, but large numbers of submarines, attributed to designers all over the world, never got further than the drawing board, and those which were completed, some of which were quite important, have not been specifically mentioned as it is considered that the submarines which have been named and described contributed the most to overall development.

Between Van Drebbel and the end of the nineteenth century somewhere between 130 and 140 designs for submarines are known to have received serious consideration, and upwards of 50 others were both designed and built, some of which were successful within the limits of the materials and scientific knowledge available in their day.

Some of the ideas put forward in the designs were most ingenious, ranging from a railway on the bottom of the sea, to boats with special doors in their bottoms to allow divers to leave the submarine temporarily to examine the sea bed. Except that they were better educated than most other people, it is curious how interested men in Holy Orders seemed to be in submarine design. Perhaps the Protestant Church felt that all the honours should not go to the Abbé Borelli. Whatever the reason, the Reverend Garrett, an Englishman, designed a submarine in 1878 and followed this a few years later with his *Resurgam*. Garrett unfortunately was unable to develop his ideas without help, and turned to Mr Nordenfeldt, a Swedish gun-maker who accepted Garrett's general ideas and, adding his own, produced three workable designs during the next eight years. These boats were built by the Naval Construction and Armament Company at Barrow-in-Furness. Two were sold to Greece and Turkey where it was found they were too difficult to operate submerged. A third was sold to Russia, but this one foundered on the surface on passage. The French attended the trials of these boats, but did not like them. They were steam-driven and gave speeds of 14 knots on the surface and 5–8 knots submerged, using reserve steam in tanks stored internally. *Nordenfeldt III* achieved a marked advance with two internal torpedo tubes.

Had this design been taken up by the British government progress might have been made which would have produced an advanced type of submarine in the British Navy, but the

The GOUBET I, 1887
A. *Trimming tank system*
a. *Conning tower*
b. *Compressed air reservoirs*
c,d. *Pumps*
h. *Water ballast*
i. *Electric accumulators*
m. *Wheel for moving propeller to port or starboard*
M. *Electric motor*
P. *Water ballast control valve*
T. *Torpedo for fixing to hull of a ship*
o. *Propeller*
x. *Safety weight*
n. *Submerging batten*

advocates of the submarine in Britain were outnumbered by the sceptics and nothing was done.

During the eight years in which Nordenfeldt was building his boats, other French designers besides Goubet were not idle. A retired Naval Constructor, Monsieur Zédé, set about collating all the best plans available to him from French Constructors. From this research he produced the *Gymnote*, in which the distinctive feature was the discharging of ballast water by compressed air. At this time the French Minister of Marine was Admiral Aube, who fully appreciated the potentialities of the *Gymnote*, and, brushing aside the prejudices of the old school of naval officers, gave the first government order for the construction of a submarine.

This was a period when French designers with their forward thinking on submarine matters were some ten years ahead of their contemporaries in other nations. Most prominent in this field was Monsieur Dupuy de Lôme, a celebrated French engineer. His was the inspiration behind the *Gymnote* and its first designer, but he died in 1885. However, Gustave Zédé completed the plans and supervised the construction, which was carried out at Toulon by his nephew, Romazotti, then a young Naval Constructor. The *Gymnote* was only 60 feet long and of 31 tons displacement, but Admiral Aube considered this would be a suitable size for coast defence and pioneered the idea that the submarine could replace much of the defensive mining which was common practice at that time. At first *Gymnote* was fitted with hydroplanes aft only, but when in 1890 the French Navy took over the boat her Commanding Officer, Lieutenant Darriens (later Vice Admiral) advised two additional pairs of hydroplanes. These were later reduced to two pairs in all. Eventually *Gymnote* was given an extensive refit in 1897–98 and provided with a new motor, a variable-pitch propeller, a new battery with lead accumulators, and two dropping gears for 14-inch torpedoes. She was never put to operational use but was invaluable as a trials boat and was not scrapped until May 1908.

In 1890 Romazotti himself submitted a new design incorporating all that was best in the *Gymnote*. Gustave Zédé died during the construction of this second boat, which was named after him. To assist better depth-keeping, hydroplanes were fitted midships as well as aft and forward, but the most striking improvement was the automatic bow cap which shut immediately a torpedo was fired. The torpedoes were 17 feet 7 inches long, but the change in balance or trim on firing could be well held by the three pairs of hydroplanes. To meet what were considered to be naval requirements of

sea-keeping and habitability the *Gustave Zédé* was 148 feet long and displaced 266 tons.

On reflection this was considered rather too big a jump in size, but in spite of difficulties the French persevered with her and made her into a sound operational submarine. Meanwhile, in 1896 the French Minister of Marine, Monsieur Lockrey, had organised a competition in response to which six complete designs were submitted. The winner was Monsieur Laubeuf with his design for the *Narval* (Plate I). The requirements were 200 tons displacement with a radius of action on the surface of 100 miles at 12 knots, and 10 miles at 8 knots when submerged. To meet the surface radius requirement Laubeuf provided steam propulsion, and employed electric battery power for submerged propulsion only, thus introducing the two-power system to Europe. Other advances were a double hull, the space between the two hulls being used for ballast water and for a system of tanks to compensate for various weights carried and consumed, such as fuel for the engines and food for the crew. The *Narval* was 111 feet long and displaced 168 tons. The range of action on the surface was 250 miles at 11 knots and 500 miles at 7.5 knots. Submerged, her batteries gave 25 miles at 6 knots and 75 miles at 5 knots. Laubeuf had definite operational requirements in mind and visualised his submarine leaving Brest or Cherbourg at night and crossing the channel on the surface for diving operations off Plymouth, Portsmouth or the Thames. The *Narval* was fully capable of fulfilling these objects. As early as 1901 she successfully forced the difficult entrance of the Brest roadstead after cruising for 48 hours in Channel. She and her sister submarines remained the undoubted leaders in submarine capability until 1905. By 1899 the French had made up their minds that the submarine was definitely the weapon of the future, and within a year produc-

ed a plan to build a submarine fleet of 39 boats partly 'Gustave Zédé' type with electric propulsion only and par of 'Narval' type with the two-power propulsion system.

Across the Atlantic meanwhile, one man had domina the advance in submarine design. This man was Mr John Holland of Paterson, New Jersey. From 1875 to 1887 Holla designed seven submarines. They were of varying sizes a met with varying fortunes, from disaster and shipwreck never getting further than the drawing board, but when 1887, Mr Whitney, Secretary of the Navy, invited designs a submarine, Holland's designs had reached No. VII. This submitted to the Navy Bureau and it was accepted. The b was planned with the two-power system of propulsion, t introducing this method to the New World. Holland exp mented with types of petrol engine instead of steam, a these were quite successful.

Whitney had in mind some alternative to the vulnerabili of torpedo boats to surface gunfire. A large number of desi were sent in, and three were accepted to be taken a st further. They were the Baker boat, the Lake boat a Holland's, all named after their designers.

Baker's boat failed on trials because the propelling syst which was linked to the diving system, prevented an e depth line being held.

That Lake's design was not finally accepted by the Uni States Navy in no way deterred this undaunted designer, he went ahead with his *Argonaut I* and *II*, concentrating a submersible which could go along the sea bed on wh and from which divers could make explorations. Within limitations *Argonaut II* was successful, and following the *Protector* was built and armed with three torpedoes. United States Navy Board considered this submarine v good for harbour defence and an improvement on min

which they liked her ability to accommodate divers
tting cables and other work on the sea bed. Much play
made of the fact that she could be connected with the
by telephone, and that there were flat surfaces of the
ed off the eastern seaboard running out as far as 175
suitable for *Argonaut II*.

land VII', which the Navy Bureau accepted, was the
ct of a good deal of wrangling in high places, and the con-
was not signed until 1895. Further delays occurred, and
not until 23rd June 1896 that the keel was laid down.
th August 1897 she was launched under the name of
er. Holland was obliged by the Navy Bureau to adopt
propulsion for surface running, fitting two triple-
sion engines driving two propellers. The considerable
power which the naval authorities attempted made
oat unhabitable on account of the high temperature,
ompletion was abandoned for some considerable time.
influenced John Holland to form the Holland Boat
any.

anwhile, Holland built his No. VIII privately in his own
any's yard. The boat was an undoubted success, and
nd placed her at the disposal of the naval authorities,
ought her. Thus a submarine entered the United States
some ten years after the French had taken this memo-
step with the *Gymnote*. She was 53 feet long, 6 feet
er than *Gymnote*, and of 75 tons displacement, that is to
louble the size. Abandoning steam, Holland placed his
in his petrol engines for surface running. There was one
do tube forward and she carried one reload. In this boat
he prototype of submarines of the United States and
t Britain for the next fifty years. In June 1900 Congress
ed the construction of six boats of improved surface
ubmerged performance ('Holland IX'), the first of which
hristened *Adder*.

Before the century ended a number of other countries had
taken positive action in submarine navigation, but none had
made any important contribution to the evolution of the
submarine. In Spain a young lieutenant, Isaac Peral, designed a boat which was launched in 1887 and was fairly
successful. She was of all-electric propulsion and had two
propellers. With a length of 70 feet and of 80 tons displacement she compared closely with Holland's boats, but Peral
gave her vertical screws for depth-keeping, following the
Nordenfeldt principle, and this inhibited acceptance by the
Spanish government. In the event, a Royal Commission decided, after the most exhaustive study of all available information on submarines, not to proceed with further construction. They did, however, reward Peral handsomely for
this work.

Russia's contribution was centred on their inventor
Drzewiecki, who came second to Laubeuf in the French competition and designed special 'drop collars' for launching
torpedoes carried externally. Italy had come to no definite
policy with the submarine as a weapon of war. Meanwhile
Germany was holding her hand, believing to some extent
that the shallow waters around her coast gave ample protec-
tion to her ports at least for the time being, and influenced by
Admiral Tirpitz's policy to build up a battle fleet at all costs.
The Japanese were just watchful, and this can also be said
for the Portuguese. In Sweden they had the great experience
of Nordenfeldt, but moved on to building a submarine
named the *Hajem* on the Holland design with a petrol engine
for surface propulsion, and in Holland itself there were plans
for building a boat on the design of their namesake. Austria
was in much the same position. That the new century would
be a momentous one in the evolution of the submarine was
certain.

The GUSTAVE ZEDE, c. 1890, running at full speed

CHAPTER V

Acceptance by the Navies of the World

The year 1900 can be taken as the dividing line betwee
age of technical experiment and reality since in the
decade the submarine was to take its place fully in the n
of the world.

Six navies now possessed a total of ten submarine:
there were another eleven under construction. In nun
France was well in the lead with a total of fourteen buil
building. She was concentrating on steam for surface pr
sion because of troubles with early internal combu
engines which had proved difficult to resolve. On the
hand America, with only two submarines, was set fair fo
future. Although the petrol engine of the 'Holland' wa
from perfect and indeed could be dangerous, its sele
for surface propulsion was only one step from the sha
things to come, namely the diesel. Both countries used ele
motors for submerged propulsion and it was clear that
method had come to stay. The Whitehead torpedo, con
to both countries' designs, was assured of its future a
primary weapon for firing from either external or int
torpedo tubes.

Great Britain so far had no submarines and was clir
now by tender threads to the Lord St Vincent doctrin
Germany Admiral Tirpitz had determined to build a k
fleet of sufficient strength to challenge British suprem
and played down the submarine on the grounds tha
German Navy would wait and see if this untried new wa:
had a future or not.

During 1901 the French still pressed ahead. Already
were experimenting with solid injection engines for su:
propulsion. More impressive, however, in their manoeu
that year was the submersible *Gustave Zédé* which atta
the French fleet leaving Ajaccio and 'torpedoed' the ba
ship *Charles Martel*. Here was something of major r
significance—the submarine could be a weapon of at
and, moreover, could operate unsupported.

The British government therefore could no longer
regard this danger, and on the excuse that the only way
efficient in anti-submarine technique was to possess the v
and study it at first hand, made the decision to intro
submarines into the British Navy.

'Close attention has been given by the Admiralty to
subject of submarine boats.' Viscount Goschen, First
of the Admiralty, had made this statement in April
Now, one year later, his successor Lord Selborne annour
'Five submarine vessels of the type invented by Mr Hol
have been ordered, the first of which should be delivered
autumn. What the future value of these boats may k
naval warfare can only be a matter of conjecture, but ex
ments with these boats will assist the Admiralty in asses
their true value.'

Already, however, the pattern was taking shape in
minds of the world's naval leaders. It was clear that
smallest type could replace some of the defensive minir
harbours. A slightly larger type could influence blocka
ships to keep their distance and possibly bring about
lifting of a blockade altogether. In the double motive-pe
large boats there was a potential attacking force, capab
operating unseen and unsupported against the enemy's c
and sea communications.

The five British 'Hollands' (Plate II), which were all bui
the works of Messrs Vickers, Son and Maxim at Barrov
Furness, in England, did not begin their lives too hap
During construction both the builders and the naval
resentative, Captain R. N. Bacon, became convinced
there must be something wrong with the drawings, ar
was decided to send for an American naval officer to ad
He, too, was certain the drawings were wrong, but the au
rities at the top decided that construction must continu
was not until *Holland I* was undergoing trials in the c
and nearly turned on end that the modifications recomm
ed were carried out and all was well. So well, in fact, tha
a few years Britain was leading the field.

The British 'Hollands', in spite of the modifications, v

almost identical to those of the United States. They were found to control well at all speeds. They carried two officers and five ratings. No periscope was supplied, so Captain Bacon produced his own design.

It must not be thought that these first five British submarines did not have their troubles after leaving the builders' yard. An early test of their capabilities was a surface trip from Portsmouth round the Isle of Wight. All five boats started together, but three were out of action by the time they got to the Spit Fort, which is only a mile or so from the entrance to the main harbour. One broke down about halfway to the well-known yachting centre at Cowes, and the fifth finally came to grief directly opposite the Royal Yacht Squadron Club House. In time these difficulties were successfully overcome, and from the 'Hollands' Britain designed her own first submarine, *A.1.*

It was *Le Matin* which now took a hand in helping the French Navy to advance further in submarine construction, by running a national subscription which raised 300,000 francs. This was presented to the nation for the construction of two submarine boats. They were built from designs of Romazotti. The first, the *Français*, was launched at Cherbourg in January 1901, and the second, named *Algérien*, in February of the following year. These were single motive-power boats with electric propulsion and single propellers and were 118 feet long with surface displacement of 143 tons, thoroughly manageable craft and efficient for their purpose of coast defence.

From this date until 1905 French submarine building, while contributing a considerable amount to the evolution of the submarine, was so varied that the exact nature of the contribution is difficult to evaluate. Under the chaotic policy of Monsieur Pelletan, Minister of Marine, France built a variety of submersibles ranging from the very small up to 800 tons displacement. Some were entirely electric-propelled, one was driven by a heavy-oil engine for both surface and submerged running. Others had gasoline engines of various types. The heavy-oil engine was never a success because of the difficulty of providing air when submerged, and the petrol engines were so dangerous that they were eventually banned altogether by the Minister of Marine. It is hardly surprising that with such constant chopping and changing no standard type emerged, but the exercising which was carried out, particularly by the 'Narval' class, enabled the French not only to define clearly the roles of their submarine force in harbour and coast defence but also to point the way to the 'overseas' submarine of the future.

It was in 1904 that Britain, through the dynamic vision of Admiral Sir John Fisher (Jackie Fisher), caught up and overtook French thinking. The following letter sums up the position in 1904 so well that it is reproduced in full. Admiral Fisher was Commander-in-Chief Portsmouth at this time.

Admiralty House,
Portsmouth.
April 20th, 1904.

My dear friend,

I will begin with the last thing in your letter, which is far the most important, and that is our paucity of submarines. I consider it the most serious thing at present affecting the British Empire. That sounds big, but it is true. Had either the Russians or the Japanese had submarines the whole face of their war would have been changed for both sides. It really makes me laugh to read of Admiral Togo's eighth attack on Port Arthur! Why! Had he possessed submarines it would have been all over with the whole Russian Fleet caught like rats in a trap. Similarly, the Japanese Admiral Togo outside would never have dared to let his transports, full of troops, persue the even tenor of their way to Chemulpo and elsewhere!

It is astounding to me, perfectly astounding, how the very best amongst us fail to realize the vast impending revolution in Naval warfare and Naval strategy that the submarine will accomplish! (I have written a paper on this but it is so violent that I am keeping it!). Here, at Portsmouth, just to take a single instance, is the battleship *Empress of India* engaged on manoeuvres and knowing of the proximity of submarines, the Flagship of the Second Admiral of the Home Fleet, nine miles beyond the Nab Light (out in the open) so self-confident of safety and so oblivious to the possibilities of modern warfare that the Admiral is smoking his cigarette, the Captain is calmly seeing defaulters on the half-deck, no one caring an iota for what is going on, and suddenly they see a Whitehead torpedo miss their stern by a few feet! And how fired? From a submarine of the 'pre-Adamite' period, small, slow, badly fitted, *with no periscope at all*, and yet this submarine followed that battleship for a solid two hours under water, coming up gingerly about a mile off every now and then like a beaver! Just to take a fresh compass bearing on her prey and then down again.

Remember that this is done (and I want specially to emphasize the point) with a Lieutenant in command of the boat out in her for the first time in his life on his own account, and half the crew never out before either. Why, it is wonderful! And so what results may we expect when bigger and faster boats and periscopes more powerful than the naked eye (such as the latest pattern one I saw the other day) and with experienced Officers and crews and with nests of the submarines acting together?

I have not disguised my opinion in season and out of season as to the essential, imperative, immediate, vital, pressing, urgent (I cannot think of any more adjectives) necessity for more submarines at once – at the very least twenty-five in addition to those now ordered and building and 100 more as soon as practicable, or we shall be caught with our breeches down just as the Russians have been!

And then, my dear friend, you have the astounding audacity to say to me: 'I presume you only think they (the submarines) can act on the defensive'!! Why, my dear fellow, not take the offensive? Good Lord! If our Admiral is worth his salt he will tow his submarines at eighteen knot speed and put them into the hostile port (like ferrets after the rabbits) before war is officially declared. Just as the Japanese acted

before the Russian Naval Officers knew that war was declared.

In all seriousness I don't think it is even faintly real the immense, impending revolution which the submar will effect as offensive weapons of war.

When you calmly sit down and work out what will hap in the narrow waters of the Channel and the Mediterran – how totally the submarines will alter the effect of Gibral Port Said, Lemnos and Malta, it makes one's hair stand end.

Yours,
J. A. FISH

Within a short space of time Admiral Fisher became F Sea Lord and set himself to following up his thoughts on s marines. Classes 'B' and 'C' followed in quick succession both made cruises around the English coast in a flot numbering seventeen boats. These led to the constructio D.1 which proved to the world that the submarine wo definitely have a major influence on sea power. D.1 was down in 1906 and completed in 1908 and was the first Bri submarine fitted with diesel engines, thus ending for country the petrol-engine era. Experimental diesel engi had been fitted in British submarines as far back as A.13, no whole class of submarines had been constructed with t type of propulsion. D.1 had far better endurance than previous boats, having a range of 2500 miles, and could steady 14½ knots on the surface at full speed. Submerged, batteries could provide power for short bursts of 10 kn She was the first British submarine with twin screws. ballast tanks were not inside the hull but fitted on the outs as 'saddle tanks', a principle which was to be followed tensively for half a century.

Because of her size she was given one stern torpedo t since it was thought that it might not be possible always turn such a large boat quickly enough to bring the bow tu to bear. The advantages of the 'D' class were capped by fitting of wireless for the first time. In these vessels the 'o seas' submarine became a reality.

World Wars

By 1914 over one hundred and thirty years had passed since Bushnell attacked the British fleet in the Hudson River. During this time the pattern of the submarine as a fighting ship had been established from the technical aspect, but its evolution as far as naval operations were concerned had progressed mostly on paper, in the writings of naval officers, and little advance had been made in practice.

When the First World War broke out the Germans, under Admiral von Tirpitz, had twenty-five operational submarines. Their task was to carry out a war of attrition against the British Grand Fleet, with the object of reducing it to parity with the German High Seas Fleet, so that a major fleet action could be fought at the will of the Germans with a reasonable chance of success. The presence of these few German submarines in the North Sea and the eastern approaches to the English Channel, and the sinking by *U.9* of the three British armoured cruisers *Hogue*, *Aboukir* and *Cressey*, made the Grand Fleet move from its base at Scapa Flow to harbours on the west coast of Scotland until anti-submarine measures had been worked up. When *U.20* actually made the north-about passage to the west coast of the British Isles in a voyage of eighteen days (the passage of the Dover Straits was by now too dangerous) the Grand Fleet again took heed, and when at sea only moved at high speed and zigzagged.

Thus in the space of a few months the submarine could hardly have done more to influence naval operations. This rapid evolution could well have stopped here, at least for the time being, but when the German naval staff heard from the Army Command, somewhat unexpectedly, that the war was likely to be a long one, it was decided to attack commerce. This decision posed a major problem. The German 'U' boats had exceeded all expectations in their capabilities of endurance and hitting power, but what they could not do without endangering themselves to an unacceptable degree was to visit and search in accordance with international law and in so doing abandon their greatest asset, namely, submergence.

Thus unrestricted warfare against commerce gradually came into being both because of its potential to win the war at sea, which the army could not do on land, and because of the submarine's vulnerability when not acting in its true element.

As the war dragged on into years instead of the originally expected months, there were many intermittent periods when the Germans eased their attack on commerce, depending on the fluctuation of international opinion. They also built the first submarine merchant ship which, in 1916, visited United States ports, demonstrating that the British blockade of German commerce could be broken by this method. The first of class was named *Deutschland* (Plate IV) and made a favourable impression on the Americans. However, after the stalemate of the battle fleets following the battle of Jutland, and the sinking of the *Lusitania* which brought America into the war on 6th April 1917, the submarine became for the first time the main weapon of a major sea power. In so doing it had evolved from a coastal defence intelligent mine to a primary warship.

During the period 1915 to mid-1917, 104 German operational submarines, out of a total strength of 148, sank over three and a half million tons of shipping, two million of which was British, and defeat for England was a mere six weeks away. At this point not only was the submarine the major weapon of German sea power but it had nearly brought the greatest sea power in the world to defeat.

Typical of these submarines was *U.35* (Plate III), commanded by Von Arnaud de la Perière, a German submarine ace, who sank over a quarter of a million tons of shipping in the Mediterranean.

By mid summer 1917 German 'U' boats were not only making the long passage to the Mediterranean without difficulty but were also reaping a harvest across the Atlantic on the eastern American seaboard. Among the submarines used were the large merchant boats converted to the 'U.151'

class which, armed with 5.9-inch guns and carrying tw
two torpedoes, could stay at sea for three months.

Naturally anti-submarine measures took the hi
priority in the British Navy, but apart from the introdu
of the convoy system, which virtually saved England, s
tific measures such as the Hydrophone had been singu
ineffective and there was nothing being developed on w
any great hopes could be pinned.

Nevertheless, the submarine had not yet replaced
battleship as the primary ship in the navies of the world
a place was found for it within the battle fleet itself i
British Navy. Great Britain built the 'K' class (Plate V) w
were three times the size and of seven times the horse-p
of any former British submarine. Two flotillas of t
magnificent boats were formed to operate with the G
Fleet, for which they needed a speed of 24 knots, achi
comfortably through the Parsons steam turbine. No op
tunity came their way to put their tactics with the fleet
practice but they accompanied the fleet until the end o
war and were unique in the evolution of the submarin

To summarise the position at the end of the war it ca
said that basically the submarine did not alter. Submar
were merely larger and improved in many ways. For exam
some submarines carried ten torpedo tubes instead of si
the two-power propulsion system remained. On the op
tional side both the two major sea powers had found the
marine ineffective for defence. For instance, none of
German raids on the English coast had been intercepte
submarines although considerable numbers had been res
ed for this purpose. Again, rather than replacing the m
submarines were used by both sides for the purpose of m
laying, particularly the Germans with their 'U.C' cl
which were the first to adapt mines for laying by means o
torpedo tubes.

What transcended all other considerations was the pr
ability to operate unsupported against the enemy's co
and in the oceans. Through the world-shattering emp
ment of unrestricted warfare, which allowed full use of
torpedo unseen instead of the surface use of the gun, the
marine was making full use of its property of submerg
and its powerful weapon, the torpedo. For good measure
mere presence of the submarine in the oceans had a ma
influence on fleets which was often simply psychologica

These advances in the operational sphere of naval war
brought the submarine to a position where its defeat
major sea power was a possibility. In all, German submar
sank 5708 ships totalling over 11 million tons and equal
one quarter of the world's shipping, over half of this t
being British. That the submarine did not win the war at
for the Germans was due firstly to the convoy system
secondly to the entry of America into the war, whereby
building rate of merchant ships exceeded the sinkings.

Before the war was over Britain built the 'M' class of wh
one boat was completed. *M.1* (Plate VII) carried one 12-i
gun, the principle being that, since the torpedo armamen
the standard submarine of the day could not sink a Dre
nought, a vessel which could bring a very big gun to bea
1000 yards range might be more effective. *M.1* was never tr
in war but, as a type, was a success.

By now the reliability of the submarine was someth
which the navies of the world accepted. Perhaps the b
example of this was the British 'H' class. First laid dowr
1915 these small handy boats of 500 tons with four 21-i
bow torpedo tubes went about their business with gr
confidence. Those built in the United States for Britain h
pily crossed the Atlantic without assistance.

When peace came Great Britain was left the undispu
major sea power and somewhat strangely began build
ingenious experimental submarines, thus developing
very weapon which had so nearly brought her to defeat. T
most successful British submarine in the war had been
'E' class, carrying two 18-inch tubes in the bow, one sin
on each beam and one single astern. It was decided t

vier torpedo armament was preferable to the 12-inch gun
he 'M' class and the submarine must be able to sink a
or war vessel. This policy resulted in the L.50 class,
ying six torpedo tubes in the bow and an increase in
of the torpedo itself from 18 inches to 21 inches.

t the same time anti-submarine measures were not over-
ked and twelve boats of the 'R' class (Plate VI) were built
h high underwater speed and a salvo of six 18-inch torpe-
s, solely to sink another submarine. Also, determined
eep the lead in construction, the hull of one of the aban-
ed 'M' class was used to build the first submarine aircraft
rier, M.2 (Plate VIII). This boat was fitted with a hangar
provided with a reconnaissance Parnell Peto seaplane
ch could be launched from the surface by catapult. The
oplane had an endurance of two hours flying time at the
of which it had to be either at its home base or back on
rd its parent submarine.*

n 1925 yet another experimental submarine was built.
s was X.1, of 3000 tons, carrying four 5.2-inch guns and a
vo of six 21-inch torpedoes. This ship was superior to the
troyer of the day and was really a commerce raider, the
type which Britain wanted to emphasize. X.1 had trouble
h her engines and so was scrapped. It is odd that the Board
dmiralty should ever have ordered the building of such a
. Belated propaganda decrying the value of this sub-
rine did not deter the French from building the Surcouf
te IX) in 1927, fitted with two 8-inch guns and carrying a
tter seaplane, her avowed prime purpose being commerce
ding.

he final British experiment was M.3, a minelayer with
reased capacity from the 18 mines carried internally in a
ndard submarine to 100 all carried externally.

ermany's part in the evolution of the submarine from the
l of the First World War was governed at first by the 1918
aty of Versailles, which allowed no submarines to be kept
the Germans and forbade the construction or acquisition
ny submarine even for commercial purposes. However, in
late nineteen-twenties she began building in Holland,
ining her crews abroad also.

Meanwhile Britain had returned to the St Vincent policy
l at the Washington Naval Conference of 1921 strongly
vocated abolition, but this was opposed, mainly by France
l the United States. While limitations of surface naval
naments were achieved in the Washington Treaty, no
it was put on the number of submarines. The next move
s made in the London Naval Treaty of 1931. The principal
val powers held this conference because the Washington
eaty of 1921 was due to expire in 1936. Again Great Britain
vocated abolition, this time supported by Italy, and some
itation in submarines was arrived at. However, a major
ange came about in 1935 when Hitler repudiated the Ver-
lles Treaty. Great Britain immediately concluded the
glo-German Naval Agreement and special provision was
de for Germany to build up to 100 per cent of British ton-
ge at some future date, should the situation warrant it. In
38 Hitler invoked this clause, although there was no justi-
ation for it and against all the protests from Britain and
er maritime nations.

Finally, after Munich, the German 'Z plan' was put into
ce which authorised the building of 300 submarines by
45 for the express purpose of defeating Great Britain. The
bmarine was again playing a most important part in inter-
tional affairs.

By the end of the nineteen-twenties British submarine
periments had died down and development in building in
e navies of the world, uncontrolled by restrictive clauses in
aties, had settled down to a standard form. The British
ncentrated on boats of 500 and 1000 tons. The United
ates with the Pacific Ocean to cover built a large 3000-ton

type, the 'V' class, carrying two 6-inch guns. The Japanese,
being the weaker naval power in that area, built up a formi-
dable submarine fleet with some boats of 2000 tons. The
French too went in for quantity and built more submarines
than either Britain or the United States.

The Second World War found the British supremely confi-
dent in the capability of the Asdic underwater detection
device for tracking submarines submerged which it was believed would drive the enemy submarines from the oceans.
This did not happen as the Germans operated on the surface
using 'wolf packs' to attack convoys at night. First they con-
centrated their force, then moved into the centre of the convoy under cover of darkness and fired their torpedoes, also
from the surface. These tactics were immediately successful
and once again the submarine came near to winning the war
at sea. That it did not do so this time was due to the Germans
sacrificing their main objectives for subsidiaries, such as aug-
menting the Italians in the Mediterranean and covering the
Norwegian coast against the possibility of an allied invasion.
To these faulty appreciations, which deprived the Atlantic
force of the means of reaching a decisive position, was added
considerable allied scientific advancements, the principal of
which was radar.

Through this invention the German 'wolf packs' were
driven from the surface and forced to dive. There was a time
when there were no enemy submarines in the Atlantic at all.
For the Germans to continue their attack on commerce with
any effect it was now necessary to increase underwater
speed so that their submarines when submerged could still
close on the convoys and then surface and complete the attack under cover of darkness. By delaying surfacing until
very close to the convoy the effect of radar was virtually
nullified, and the Asdic, at best, had only a couple of miles or
so in which to warn the Commodore of the convoy.

Meanwhile, through the schnorkel tube, an invention
which the Germans were the first to put to practical use and
whereby the submarine could take in air to its diesel engines
when submerged, greater underwater endurance was ob-
tained. The top of the schnorkel tube was difficult to spot on
radar and when in use the boats were still in comparative
safety.

Coupled with this improvement, which greatly conserved
battery power, the Germans doubled the electric power for
submerged propulsion, necessitating larger electric batteries which in turn dictated the size of the submarines. In
some cases this too was doubled, but this was not a disad-
vantage because these longer boats were better for stream-
lining.

The Germans named these types 'XXI' and 'XXIII'. Both
classes could do 18 knots submerged, a speed well sufficient
to intercept convoys. Later the German Professor Walther
produced an engine for submerged propulsion which ran on
a high concentration of hydrogen peroxide – 'ingolin'. This
engine, by reason of needing no air, brought the development
of the true submarine vessel a stage nearer, but the war
ended before a force fitted with these engines, type 'XXVI',
could be got to sea.

Whereas the schnorkel allowed German submarines to
patrol for three weeks off the Cape of Good Hope, the Walther
boats, type 'XXVI', would have had a greater impact on
operations and if they had been disposed to the best advan-
tage to attack commerce they might well have become
decisive.

Typical German submarines of the Second World War were
the 'VIIB' class, of which U.99 was one (Plate X). This submarine was commanded by Otto Kretschmer, now Admiral
Commanding the German Naval Forces.

In the Pacific the Americans made the most of the submarine's offensive power by using it against the enemy fleet,
as well as the merchant fleet. In their war against Japan,
United States submarines sank one third of the Japanese
Navy, the greatest tonnage of warships ever sunk by submarines, thus elevating the submarine to the position of the

Both M.1 and M.2 were lost on diving patrols. The former was hit by a
rchant ship and the latter sank because the hangar door was opened too
n when surfacing to fly off the aircraft.

principal warship of a major sea power. Typical of the submarines which achieved this success was the *Balao* (Plate XI).

The Japanese were not so successful, either against warships or commerce. They had difficulty in finding their targets and built eleven submarines each carrying a small reconnaissance seaplane in an endeavour to improve this position. Towards the end of the war the Japanese built five large aircraft carriers (Plate XIII) offensively armed with three bombers. This force actually set out to bomb the Panama Canal, only to be halted by the war coming to an end.

During the war Great Britain, Italy, Japan and Germany all built midget submarines of various designs, or derivatives of this type of weapon such as human torpedoes. It was like going back to the days of Bushnell. The first attack was made in 1940 by the Italians on ships in the entrance to the Admiralty harbour at Gibraltar which was unsuccessful. The most famous attack was made by British 'X' craft (Plate XII), in 1943, on the German Battleship Tirpitz lying in Kåfjord in northern Norway. Two of these midget submarines were successful and the battleship was badly damaged. Earlier, in 1941, Italian human torpedoes had attacked and damaged the British battleships *Queen Elizabeth* and *Valiant* in Alexandria harbour. The Japanese took five midget submarines to Pearl Harbour but they were unsuccessful. Towards the end of the war British midgets in the Far East cut cables and attacked Japanese warships with success. The Germans also tried midgets; their '*Seehunds*' were used during the allied invasion of Europe but, although well designed, never succeeded operationally. All these attacks were worthwhile but the midgets were specialised craft and did not advance the evolution of the submarine proper.

Once again summarising the evolution of the submarine at the end of a world war, it can be said that it had proved itself equal to, if not superior to, any surface warship in the major task of sinking the enemy's heavy ships.

In operations against commerce its power was temporarily restricted by radar, but with the introduction of type 'XXVI' this could have been largely overcome and again the submarine might have been decisive.

Thus in both spheres of naval warfare, the sinking of enemy naval ships and enemy commerce, in the hands of the Americans and the Germans respectively in the Second World War the submarine had become the supreme warship.

he Nuclear Age

On 17th January 1955 the U.S.S. *Nautilus* left the Electric Boat Company's pier at Groton, Connecticut, and silently moved out into the Thames river. As she swung into the main channel she flashed the dramatic signal, 'Under way on nuclear power.'

Since the end of the Second World War the victorious powers had experimented with the various types of captured German submarines allotted to them following the division and dispersion of the German fleet. The Russians introduced a full-scale building programme, outstripping all other countries in numbers of conventionally-powered, schnorkel-equipped, ocean-going submarines, and by 1960 had a fleet of 450 boats. In contrast, the United States went steadily along the course of improved propulsion systems. She was well equipped to do this with her undamaged shipyards, her research facilities and her money. Great Britain did much the same but on a smaller scale and, as not uncommonly, achieved the earlier greater success, particularly with the Walther power plant, and in two unarmed boats, *Explorer* and *Excalibur*, achieved underwater speeds of 25 knots.

Meanwhile, behind all this varied effort there was always the certainty that one day nuclear power could be applied to the submarine, thus bringing into being at long last the true submarine which could virtually remain submerged for ever, and completing its evolution. One man who brought this dream to practical life was Rear Admiral Hyman Rickover, U.S.N., an engineer and a submariner. In 1946 Rickover was a Captain. He had before him much preliminary work by Dr Ross Gunn of the Naval Research Laboratory and Dr Philip H. Abelson of the Carnegie Institute.

The project of a nuclear reactor took root at Park Ridge, Tennessee, and for nine years Rickover overcame doubt, hostility, apathy, lack of funds, lack of materials, and much else besides. During this time he was passed over for promotion, and only at the last moment, when the submarine reactor was on the verge of completion, did the authorities begin to realise what this man had done for the United States, and, indeed, for the world. The name of Rickover will go down in the history of the submarine with those of Fulton, Laubeuf and Holland.

Nautilus (Plate XIV) was 320 feet long and of 3539 tons surface displacement. She carried six bow torpedo tubes with three reloads. She was a complete success. In May 1955 she sailed submerged from New London, Connecticut, to San Juan, Puerto Rico, a distance of 1381 miles, at an average submerged speed of 16 knots. In comparison with any other boat this was ninety times longer than any submarine had ever steamed at such high speed submerged. In short, all submarine records were broken. But most of all, here was the true submarine which need never surface, possessing a power plant which could run without air and required fuel only once every couple of years. All this might have been brought to naught but for the parallel advance in air purifying, nicknamed by the Americans 'the CO_2 Scrubber', and equally important advances in the generation of oxygen.

Nautilus was also fitted with diesel engines for use in case anything went wrong with the nuclear reactor. Because of the diesel she had a schnorkel by which the air in the boat could be completely changed in twenty minutes if operational conditions allowed.

Since she had no need to fill much of the boat with oil fuel tanks and batteries, there was room for every improvement in living conditions for her crew of ten officers and ninety-three men. There were bunks for everyone, air conditioning to keep the interior between 68 and 72 degrees Fahrenheit, and the humidity at an even 50 per cent. There were clothes-washing machines, laboratories, and a library with 600 books.

After two years *Nautilus* had steamed more than 62,500 miles, 36,500 of which had been submerged. The time had come to make history once again, and under the command of Commander William R. Anderson in August 1958 the submarine passed over the North Pole under ice. Without altering course, one moment she was steaming due north, and the next her head was due south. Before this remarkable voyage had taken place the project had received the attention of innumerable senior officers, senators, scientists and the President himself. This was not merely because of the novelty of the idea, but by making this passage and thus linking the Atlantic and Pacific Oceans all the year round, strategic thinking in the navies of the world had been changed.

From these beginnings the first production model nuclear attack submarines were built: *Skate*, *Swordfish*, *Sargo* and *Seadragon* were all commissioned before the end of 1959. All four had similar power plants which, through technical advances, had been made smaller than the original in *Nautilus*. Moreover, the boats themselves were smaller—268 feet instead of 321, and 2550 tons instead of 3539. *Skate*, the first off the production line, lost no time in establishing her name in history as she succeeded in surfacing through the ice at the North Pole.

Thoughts now turned to adapting the nuclear submarine to the needs of the Navy as a whole. It was recalled that in the spring of 1944, around Okinawa, 34 radar picket ships and supporting gunboats were sunk. Some 300 more were damaged, with the total loss of 4000 men killed and 5000 wounded. Submersible radar picket ships could have saved this loss of life. The result was the U.S.S. *Triton*, launched in August 1958 and commissioned a little more than a year later. *Triton* was the largest and most powerful submarine of her day. She was powered by two nuclear reactors, and is still the only submarine with two. The size of a light cruiser, 5700 tons on the surface and 8000 submerged, and with a length of 447½ feet, she was a monster. With 15 officers and 159 men in her crew, of whom 33 were Chief Petty Officers, she carried more talent than any previous submarine. Obviously something special and spectacular had to come from this magnificent boat. High level conferences were called, and at the conclusion Captain Beach, the Commanding Officer, was ordered to circumnavigate the globe submerged. Between 16th February and 25th April 1960 *Triton* went round the world, including an additional 2000 miles to transfer a sick rating to a surface ship, which was done without bringing the pressure hull above water, so keeping to the letter of the order. The time-table of this historic underwater voyage is worthy of record:

February	16	Submerged off Long Island.
	24	Off St Paul Rocks. Cross the equator.
March	5	Partially surfaced off Montevideo to disembark sick rating.
	7	Rounded Cape Horn.
	13	Passed Easter Island.
	25	Passed Hawaiian Islands.
	28	Passed Guam.
April	1	Passed Philippine Islands.
	5	Passed through Lombok Strait, Indonesia.
	17	Round Cape of Good Hope.
	25	Passed St Paul Rocks and completed submerged navigation of globe.

Meanwhile throughout the 1950s some quiet thinking had been going on. Minds went back to the 'Hollands' and their interesting shape. The primary objective of this decade of study was speed under water. For the public it was announced that nuclear submarines were capable of speeds of over 20 knots. This statement stands today and rightly, because it would not be in the interest of the Western World to say more, but it can be assumed that the most modern nuclear submarines are capable of speeds well over the official 20 knots. The British publication *Jane's Fighting Ships* gives U.S.S. *Skipjack* a speed of 35 knots submerged.

It was the shape of the 'Holland' boats which inspired the designers to build the *Albacore* entirely for hydrodynamic research. Hitherto, except for the British 'R' class, all sub-

marines were in fact submersibles designed principally surface ship capabilities, especially in the ratio bet length and breadth. *Albacore* was designed purely for u water work with a length/breadth ratio of 3:1 instead o 5 or 6:1 of the submersibles. In addition *Albacore* was gi very small superstructure and was powered only by ele batteries. She did her job well and her performance le designers to build the U.S.S. *Skipjack* (Plate XV). They this boat a blunt nose, shaped her like a rugby football stripped her of the normal casing and upper deck fit while retaining the large fin superstructure and for hydroplanes. She was a true submarine in basic shape marked a clear step forward in evolution. *Skipjack* v further from her predecessors in that she was given onl propeller which was slow-moving, the intention bein cut down noise.

When *Skipjack* did her trials in August 1959 she went de for longer than any previous submarine. The scene was set to build an underwater navy. There was much for thinking to do. The Soviets had put a man into space, their rocketry had developed to fantastic proportions. T submarine fleet, hitherto an enlargement of Second W War types, would shortly be turning to nuclear power. Americans determined on two immediate projects.

Following successful trials in the 1950s with 'Reg missiles in conventional submarines they built the *Hal* the first nuclear submarine to have missile armament. but* was the same size as *Triton* and had to surface to fire missiles. It was intended that she would operate in the Pa Secondly, 'killer' submarines were needed to hunt destroy enemy nuclear submarines, and for this purpose built the *Tullibee*, the smallest of the nuclear submarin displacement. Even so, she was of 2318 tons on the surf She was packed with sonar equipment. Both these ships commissioned in 1960.

Up to this time the Americans had behaved in the 1 and early 1960s rather as the French did at the end of nineteenth century and the British after the First W War, by building numerous different submarines. The had come to standardise, as the Germans did in the World War. Accordingly, *Thresher* was designed from best of *Skipjack* and *Tullibee*.

Thresher was lost in a disaster in 1963, so the *Permit* next ship in sequence, became the named ship of the clas which 22 were laid down at once, and these added to b many as 34 'Sturgeon' class, an improved version of 'Permit' class. All these submarines are supplied with pelled missiles and homing torpedoes, launched from th torpedo tubes. Experiments and exercises with the firs these two classes have changed all the old concepts of n warfare. Indeed, the war at sea in the future will be fo primarily under water in three dimensions.

All these spectacular advances in the evolution of the marine, it might be supposed, would have placed the Wes World under a sure shield of United States sea power, bu power had to take note of the advent of nuclear weapons. disturbing Russian advance in the strategic missile f widened by their putting the first 'sputnik' into orbit their programme of atmospheric tests of nuclear weap set the United States on a further programme. The b policy had been considered in the days of the building of *Nautilus* and kept in cold storage. Now, in the late 1950 was quickly unfrozen. Hitherto the nuclear subma programme had been one of 'attack', but now the submari were to be used as the greatest weapon for defence and t developed into what has been called 'the ultimate deterre

It was as far back as 1955 that a junior admiral, Will F. Raborn, was selected to develop a dependable strat ballistic missile and the submarine to launch it 'within next ten years'. With the danger signs already develop before his eyes, Admiral Raborn decided that ten years too long. Soon this thinking was reflected in the minds of Chief of Naval Operations and the Secretary of the N

orn's project was made top priority. Like Rickover he
a man who knew how to get a job done, and in his task he
equally successful. On 20th July 1960, years ahead of
dule, an American submarine fired two Polaris missiles
e entirely submerged. The missiles hurtled 1100 miles
n the Atlantic missile range with perfect accuracy. On
December of the same year, the U.S. Submarine *George*
hington (Plate XVI) sailed from Charleston, South
olina, to patrol for two months somewhere in the North
ntic. This great ship, of 5960 tons surface displacement
armed with 16 Polaris missiles, was the most powerful
ship the world had ever known and in her primary role
eploying the deterrent is virtually immune from anti-
marine measures. She has been followed by no less than
hers of similar, but latterly improved, capability which,
n deployed, will present a deterrent force of unmatched
nitude.

all this, Great Britain, for so long the greatest sea
er, has followed suit and now possesses seven nuclear
marines, four of which will be Polaris-armed, and has
rs under construction. The French, too, do not intend
r part in the evolution of the submarine to fade entirely
are moving in the same direction.

us the submarine has now come full circle. From Bourne
Van Drebbel's peaceful experiment to its development as
rship in the nineteenth century, mostly by the versatile
nch, it became in the early 1900s the weapon of the weaker
er, and later, through two world wars, it was found to be
ar winner' in the hands of major Powers. Now, in the
nd half of the twentieth century, the submarine carries
aps the greatest responsibility of all time, for on its
ence in the oceans the peace of the world chiefly depends.

Notes
1. S B = Submersible. A vessel operating on the two propulsion system.
   S M = A true submarine. A vessel operating on one propulsion system
   and having no need to surface.
   British R (No. 8) has been classified as both S B and S M as it was
   the nearest approach to the true submarine before the advent of
   nuclear power.
2. All S Bs (i.e. Nos. 1–13 inclusive) relied on electric battery power for
   submerged propulsion.
3. The statistics in the table are given as a background to the text and the
   information is relevant to the development of the story. The table does not
   represent all known facts and figures of the submarines selected.

NATIONALITY	DATE	TYPE	LENGTH BEAM DRAUGHT	DISPLACEMENT (tons) SURFACE	SUBMERGED	ENGINES
1. FRENCH	1898 1899	Narval S B	111' 6" 12' 4" 5' 3"	106	168	Steam triple expansion one s
2. BRITISH	1901 1902	Holland S B	63' 6" 11' 10" 5' 6"	105	120	Petrol one screw
3. GERMAN	1914	U 35 S B	212' 20'	685	844	Diesel twin screws
4. GERMAN	1916	Merchant ship U 151 S B	213' 29' 15'	1512	1875	Diesel twin screws
5. BRITISH	1917	K 26 S B	351' 28' 16' 10"	1750	2450	Parsons and Br Curtis steam turbines two scr
6. BRITISH	1918	R S B S M	163' 15' 9" 10'	410	500	Diesel one screw
7. BRITISH	1918	M 1 S B	305' 28' 15' 9"	1650	1950	Diesel twin screws
8. BRITISH	1920	M 2 S B	305' 28' 15' 9"	1650	1950	Diesel twin screws
9. FRENCH	1929	Surcouf S B	360' 29' 6" 23'	3304	4218	Diesel twin screws
10. GERMAN	1940	U 99 S B	218' 20' 15'		857	Diesel electric twin screws
11. AMERICAN	1942	Balao S B	307' 27' 17' 6"	1800	2455	4 diesel electric c two shafts
12. BRITISH	1943	X Craft Midget	51' 8' 6" 10'	35		Diesel
13. JAPANESE	1944	I 400 S B	380' 39' 23'	5223	6560	4 sets diesel on tv shafts
14. AMERICAN	1954	Nautilus S M	338' 29' 22'	3765	4260	Nuclear twin screws
15. AMERICAN	1958	Skipjack S M	252' 32' 28'	3075	3500	Nuclear one screw
16. AMERICAN	1959	George Washington S M	382' 33' 29'	6010	6700	Nuclear one screw

See notes on page 35

...PEDO TUBES	GUNS	OTHER	COMPLEMENT		PERFORMANCE (knots)		REMARKS
			OFFICERS	RATINGS	SURFACE	SUBMERGED	
...75" each side ...r deck	–	–	14		9.8	5.3	Torpedoes fired from 2 Drzewiecki upper deck frames each side
	–	–	2	7	8.5	7	Originally designed without a periscope
...7" ...w 2 stern	1 or 2 3.4" or 1 4.1"	–	32–39		16.4	9.7	Typical first World War
...).7"	2 5.9" or 2 4.1"	–	56		12.4	5.2	*Merchant ship Deutschland made 2 voyages to USA in 1916. Converted to U cruiser
...bow ...beam	2 4" 1 3" AA	–	5	45	23.5	10	Designed to operate with Fleet.
...bow	–	–	2	20	$9\frac{1}{2}$	15	First anti submarine submarine
...bow	1 12" Mark IX 1 3" AA		6	59	14	8	The only big gun submarine
...bow	1 3" AA	1 Parnell Peto Seaplane	6 2 air crew	59	14 3840 @ 10	8	First submersible aircraft carrier
...) mm internal ...ow, 2 stern) ...) mm external ...evolving ...ntings	2 8", 2 37 mm cannon AA, 48 mm AA.	1 Besson MB 411 two-seater seaplane.	8	110	18	$8\frac{1}{2}$	Cruiser type commerce destroyer. Seaplane had a range of 215 miles at 81 mph
...bow ...stern	1 3.5" 1 20 mm AA		44		$17\frac{1}{2}$	10	Schnorkel tube added later. Also 3.5" gun removed 1 37 mm and 1 extra 20 mm AA added.
...bow ...stern	1 4.5" 2 40 mm AA		8	75	18	9	Typical of US submersibles World War II with both submerged and surface capabilities. 12 000 mile radius of action, Fitted with radar.
...ddle charges ...ns of amatex			3 1 qualified diver	1	$6\frac{1}{2}$	5	Surface endurance 1500 @ 4. Submerged 80 @ 2.
...bow	1 5.5" 10 25 mm AA	3 Bombers (total armament 4 torpedoes, 3 800 kg & 12 250 kg bombs).	144		30 000 m @ 16 K^n 37 000 m @ 14 K^n		The largest *submersible* ever built and the largest submersible aircraft carrier.
...bow			10	95	20	23	Nuclear powered prototype
...bow			8	85	20	35	Hunter Killer
...bow	16 missile launching tubes		12	100	20	28	Polaris. The 'Ultimate Deterrent'.

The colour plates

Narval 1898–9

French

LENGTH O/A: 111 ft 6 in

BEAM: 12 ft 4 in

DRAUGHT: 5 ft 3 in

DISPLACEMENT
Surface: 106 tons
Submerged: 168 tons

ARMAMENT
Torpedo tubes: Four 17.75-in

PROPULSION
Surface: Steam
Submerged: Electric

SPEED
Surface: 9.8 knots
Submerged: 5.3 knots

COMPLEMENT: 14

Holland Class 1901–2

British

LENGTH O/A: 63 ft 6 in

BEAM: 11 ft 10 in

DRAUGHT: 5 ft 6 in

DISPLACEMENT
Surface: 105 tons
Submerged: 120 tons

ARMAMENT
Torpedo tubes: One 18-in

PROPULSION
Surface: Petrol
Submerged: Electric

SPEED
Surface: 8.5 knots
Submerged: 7 knots

COMPLEMENT
Officers: 2
Ratings: 7

U 35 1914

German

LENGTH O/A: 212 ft

BEAM: 20 ft

DRAUGHT: 12 ft

DISPLACEMENT
Surface: 685 tons
Submerged: 844 tons

ARMAMENT
Torpedo tubes: Four 19.7-in
Guns: One or two 3.4-in or one 4.1-in

PROPULSION
Surface: Diesel
Submerged: Electric

SPEED
Surface: 16.4 knots
Submerged: 9.7 knots

COMPLEMENT: 32–39

Deutschland 1916

German

LENGTH O/A: 213 ft

BEAM: 29 ft
DRAUGHT: 15 ft

DISPLACEMENT
Surface: 1512 tons
Submerged: 1875 tons

ARMAMENT (on conversion)
Torpedo tubes: Two 19.7-in
Guns: Two 5.9-in or two 4.1-in

PROPULSION
Surface: Diesel
Submerged: Electric

SPEED
Surface: 12.4 knots
Submerged: 5.2 knots

COMPLEMENT: 56

British

K 26 1917

LENGTH O/A: 351 ft

BEAM: 28 ft

DRAUGHT: 16 ft 10 in

DISPLACEMENT
Surface: 1750 tons
Submerged: 2450 tons

ARMAMENT
Torpedo tubes: Ten 18-in
Guns: Two 4-in, one 3-in AA

PROPULSION
Surface: Steam
Submerged: Electric

SPEED
Surface: 23.5 knots
Submerged: 10 knots

COMPLEMENT
Officers: 5
Ratings: 45

R Class 1918

British

LENGTH O/A: 163 ft

BEAM: 15 ft 9 in

DRAUGHT: 10 ft

DISPLACEMENT
Surface: 410 tons
Submerged: 500 tons

ARMAMENT
Torpedo tubes: Six 18-in

PROPULSION
Surface: Diesel
Submerged: Electric

SPEED
Surface: 9.5 knots
Submerged: 15 knots

COMPLEMENT
Officers: 2
Ratings: 20

M1 1918

British

LENGTH O/A: 305 ft

BEAM: 28 ft

DRAUGHT: 15 ft 9 in

DISPLACEMENT
Surface: 1650 tons
Submerged: 1950 tons

ARMAMENT
Torpedo tubes: Four 18-in
Guns: One 12-in, one 3-in AA

PROPULSION
Surface: Diesel
Submerged: Electric

SPEED
Surface: 14 knots
Submerged: 8 knots

COMPLEMENT
Officers: 6
Ratings: 59

British

M 2 1920

LENGTH O/A: 305 ft

BEAM: 28 ft

DRAUGHT: 15 ft 9 in

DISPLACEMENT
Surface: 1650 tons
Submerged: 1950 tons

ARMAMENT
Torpedo tubes: Four 18-in
Guns: One 3-in AA
Other: One seaplane

PROPULSION
Surface: Diesel
Submerged: Electric

SPEED
Surface: 14 knots
Submerged: 8 knots

COMPLEMENT
Officers: 6
Ratings: 59
Other: 2 Air crew

Surcouf 1929

French

LENGTH O/A: 360 ft

BEAM: 29 ft 6 in

DRAUGHT: 23 ft

DISPLACEMENT
Surface: 3304 tons
Submerged: 4218 tons

ARMAMENT
Torpedo tubes: Ten 550/400-mm
Guns: Two 8-in, two 37-mm AA, four 8-mm AA

Other: One seaplane

PROPULSION
Surface: Diesel
Submerged: Electric

SPEED
Surface: 18 knots
Submerged: 8.5 knots

COMPLEMENT
Officers: 8
Ratings: 110

U 99 1940

German

LENGTH O/A: 218 ft

BEAM: 20 ft

DRAUGHT: 15 ft

DISPLACEMENT
Surface: 753 tons
Submerged: 857 tons

PROPULSION
Surface: Diesel electric
Submerged: Electric

SPEED
Surface: 17.5 knots
Submerged: 10 knots

COMPLEMENT: 44

ARMAMENT
Torpedo tubes: Five 21-in
Guns: One 3.5-in, one 20-mm AA

Balao 1942

American

LENGTH O/A: 307 ft

BEAM: 27 ft

DRAUGHT: 17 ft 6 in

DISPLACEMENT
Surface: 1800 tons
Submerged: 2455 tons

ARMAMENT
Torpedo tubes: Ten 21-in
Guns: One 4.5-in, two 40-mm AA

PROPULSION
Surface: Diesel electric
Submerged: Electric

SPEED
Surface: 18 knots
Submerged: 9 knots

COMPLEMENT
Officers: 8
Ratings: 75

SS 285

British

X Craft 1943

LENGTH O/A: 51 ft

BEAM: 8 ft 6 in

DRAUGHT: 10 ft

DISPLACEMENT
Surface: 35 tons

ARMAMENT
Two saddle charges, two tons of amatex

PROPULSION
Surface: Diesel
Submerged: Electric

SPEED
Surface: 6.5 knots
Submerged: 5 knots

COMPLEMENT
Officers: 3
Ratings: 2

I 400 1944

Japanese

LENGTH O/A: 380 ft

BEAM: 39 ft

DRAUGHT: 23 ft

DISPLACEMENT
Surface: 5223 tons
Submerged: 6560 tons

ARMAMENT
Torpedo tubes: Eight 21-in

Guns: One 5.5-in, ten 25-mm AA
Other: Three bombers

PROPULSION
Surface: Diesel
Submerged: Electric

PERFORMANCE
30,000 miles at 16 knots
37,000 miles at 14 knots

COMPLEMENT: 144

Nautilus 1954

American

LENGTH O/A: 338 ft

BEAM: 29 ft

DRAUGHT: 22 ft

DISPLACEMENT
Surface: 3765 tons
Submerged: 4260 tons

ARMAMENT
Torpedo tubes: Six 21-in

PROPULSION: Nuclear

SPEED
Surface: 20 knots
Submerged: 23 knots

COMPLEMENT
Officers: 10
Ratings: 95

Skipjack 1958

American

PROPULSION: Nuclear

SPEED
Surface: 20 knots
Submerged: 35 knots

COMPLEMENT
Officers: 8
Ratings: 85

LENGTH O/A: 252 ft

BEAM: 32 ft

DRAUGHT: 28 ft

DISPLACEMENT
Surface: 3075 tons
Submerged: 3500 tons

ARMAMENT
Torpedo tubes: Six 21-in

George Washington 1959　　　American

PROPULSION: Nuclear

SPEED
Surface: 20 knots
Submerged: 28 knots

COMPLEMENT
Officers: 12
Ratings: 100

LENGTH O/A: 382 ft

BEAM: 33 ft

DRAUGHT: 29 ft

DISPLACEMENT
Surface: 6010 tons
Submerged: 6700 tons

ARMAMENT
Torpedo tubes: Six 21-in
Other: Sixteen missile launching tubes